THE OFFICIAL LEGO® CITY ANNUAL

CONTENTS

POLICE PUZZLE

Join the police and complete the sudoku grid, so that each suspect appears only once in each row and each column. Use the letters at the bottom of the page to help you complete the puzzle.

PRISON COMPETITION

Ron Bar and his buddies have spent a lot of time behind bars.
To fight boredom they play noughts and crosses. Try playing this game
with a friend. The player who gets three noughts or crosses in a row wins.

MYSTERIOUS VEHICLE

The Chief Police Officer has received news that the LEGO® CITY force is to get a new vehicle. Unfortunately, the printer has run out of ink and no one knows what it's going to be. Connect the numbers to find out what it is.

AMBUSH

SCULPTURE CONTEST

Artists look forward all year to the Annual LEGO CITY Sculpture Contest – and art lovers flock from miles around to see the amazing statues! Can you spot the Red Scarf Crook causing mischief?

You found him again! Wow!
It's time for another challenge, then.
Look carefully at this picture
and try to find ten tiny differences
from the first image.

PIZZA DELIVERY MAN

B.

A.

D.

C.

Philip, the pizza delivery man, loves watching horror films, even though he is afraid of his own shadow. Look at the shadows in the frames and work out which one belongs to Philip.

CHEESE STRETCHING!

These children are having fun stretching the cheese from their pizzas. Follow the cheese lines and help them find their plates.

VIDEO FRAME

What has the camera filmed? Use the following information to find the correct picture:
- There is no bike mechanic.
- There is a boy with his skateboard.
- There is no girl.

THE TRICK

HIGH-SPEED CHASE

4. The police officers patrol the streets in their:
a) police car
b) cable car

2. When you witness an accident you have to file:
a) a statement
b) your nails

1. In order to track down a culprit, the police lead:
a) an old lady across the street
b) an investigation

ON THE RUN

Read this phone report and draw the route the robber takes to escape. Put 'X' where he's hiding.

. . . HE RAN OUT OF THE JEWELLER'S AND ACROSS THE CAR PARK. HEADING TOWARDS THE PHONE BOOTH. HE PASSED BY THE HOT-DOG STAND AND FELL STRAIGHT INTO THE FOUNTAIN, THEN HE RAN ROUND THE BENCH TOWARDS THE PARK AND I LOST SIGHT OF HIM . . .

UNLUCKY ESCAPE

START

Collect all the scattered loot and find
out where the robber has escaped to.
Be careful not to step in any oily puddles.

IDENTIKIT

The LEGO CITY Police use identikit pictures to identify criminals.
Can you join together the correct halves of these identikit pictures?
Then, draw your own in the frame below!

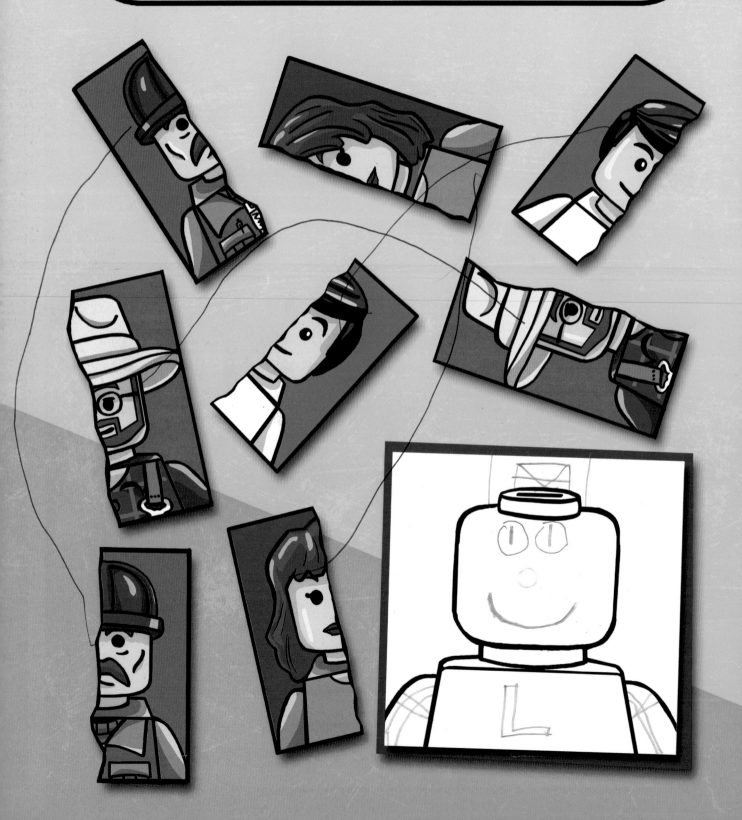

CITY AT NIGHT

The night patrol keeps the city safe at night, but it's not only the police officers who are awake. Look at these two pictures and work out what ~~five~~ things have been changed while the police weren't looking.

Six

POLICE STATION

High alert at the LEGO CITY police station! There's been a prison break and the police need to get all the escaped criminals back behind bars. Can you help them by spotting the Red Scarf Crook?

PN 7288

BEAR ATTACK!

Famous butterfly researcher, Professor Hans Wing, has met a bear while exploring in the forest. Now he needs your help! Using the pattern on the left as your guide, add lines to complete the honeycomb on the right and distract the bear.

STATION PRANK

What a lark! The jokers at the forest fire station have put two very similar cups next to Albert Match's trophy. Compare them with the one he remembers to work out which one is his.

SOUND THE ALARM!

Chuck Smoke has received an emergency call from Professor Wing. He's now stuck up a tree! Help Smoke sound the alarm by circling the items he can use to wake up his sleeping friends.

RESCUE MISSION

The firefighters had better hurry if they're going to cushion Professor Wing's fall! Connect the dots from 1 to 8 to create a safety net for the dangling scientist.

NUMBER PUZZLE

PL 7803
BL 4208
PL 7296
JK 4503

Lieutenant Smoke is trying to write a report on which of the fire vehicles haven't been washed yet. Help him read the number plate of the truck and then circle it on his piece of paper.

LUNCH BREAK

A TOUGH DECISION

Break down and cry.

Call the fire brigade.

Run as fast as he can.

Put out the fire.

Roast a sausage.

Oh no! A fire has broken out in the forest! Professor Wing needs to act quickly. What do you think he should do? Tick the correct box from the options above to help him make his decision.

FULLY EQUIPPED

FIRE!!!

Having been called by the professor, the firefighters are on their way to help. Draw a line from each question mark to the correct item in the box above, so that each of them has the same equipment.

STATION SIGNALS

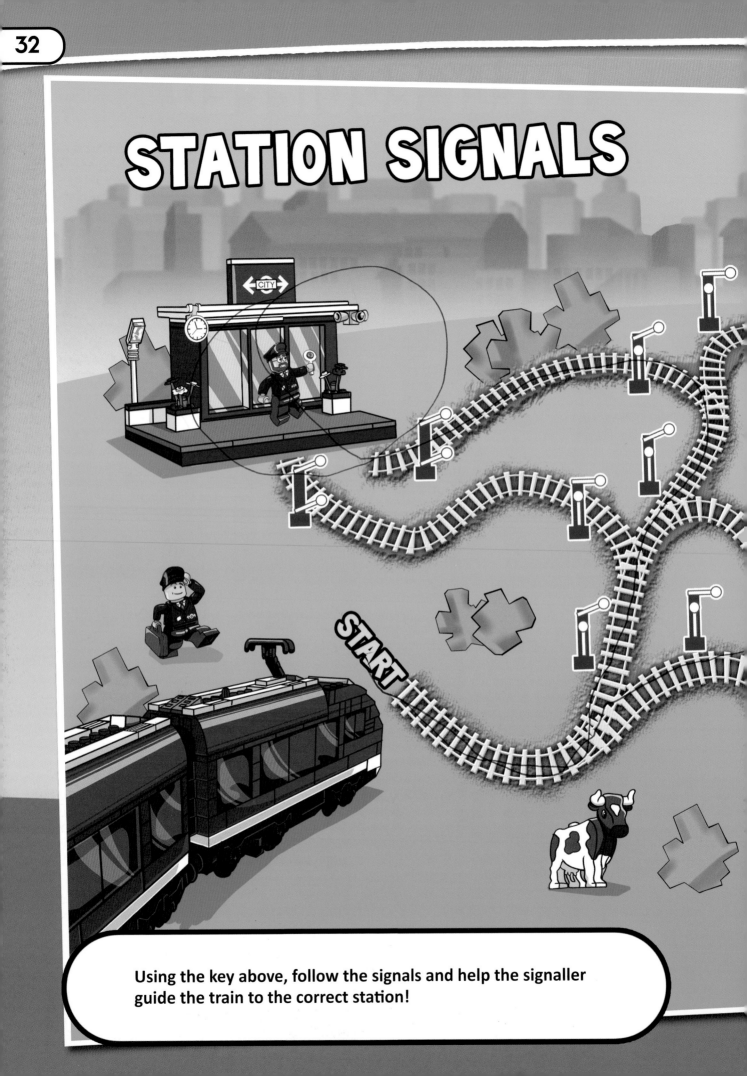

START

Using the key above, follow the signals and help the signaller guide the train to the correct station!

STOP!

GO AHEAD!

SLOW DOWN!

ALWAYS ON TIME

Ms Penny is always impressed by Walter Goldenrail's punctuality!
Can you draw lines between the pairs of clocks that show the same time?

EXPRESS TRAIN

Everything can change in a flash at the railway station!
Look at these two pictures and find five differences between them.

STATION SEQUENCE

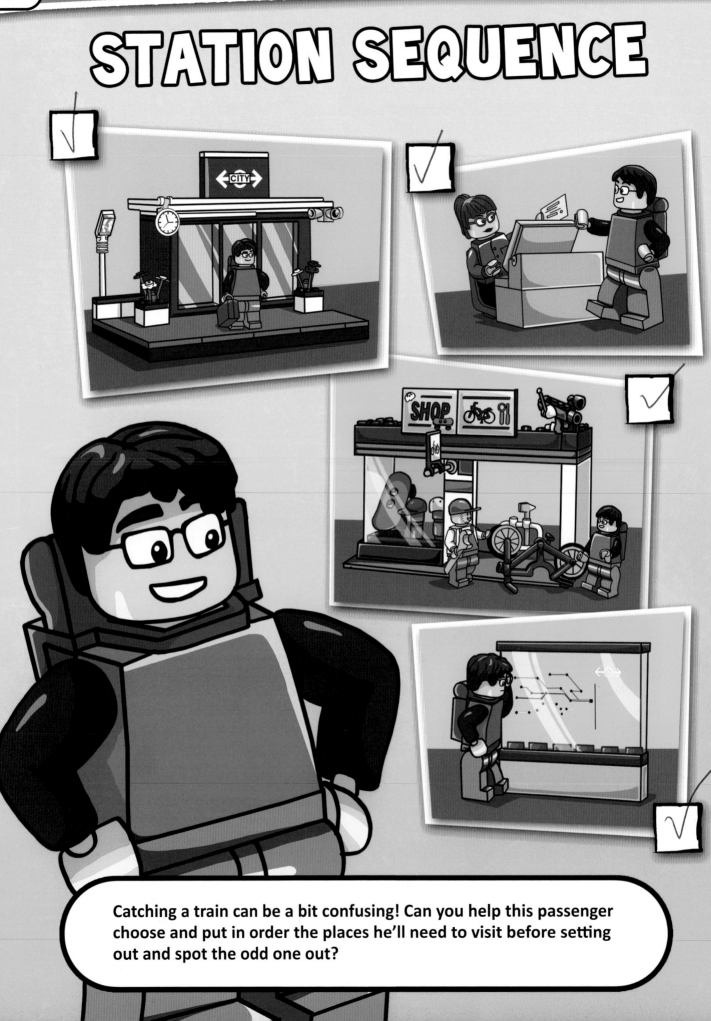

Catching a train can be a bit confusing! Can you help this passenger choose and put in order the places he'll need to visit before setting out and spot the odd one out?

SAFE LANDING

NIGHT GEAR

Surviving a night in the forest isn't so difficult, as long as you come prepared! Look at the policemen's equipment, and put a check mark next to the items you think they need.

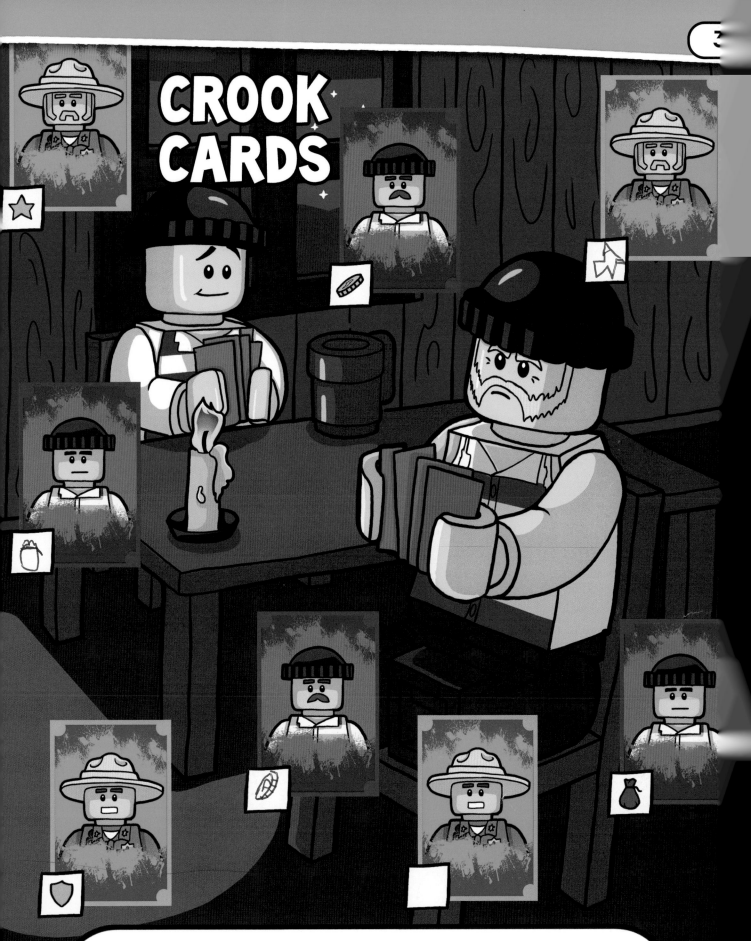

CROOK CARDS

Meanwhile, at their old hiding place, crooks Sam and Burt have also decided to wait out the night. To pass the time, they're playing a card game called 'Cops and Robbers'. Find the matching pairs of cards, and mark the empty boxes with the right symbols.

THE SECRET LETTER

○ in the 𝖾𝖺𝗌𝗍 ┼ and ⊙ before the ⌣

⊘

KEY

◎	I went to the camp
✳	Help
⌣	Valley
⊙	Stop
∿	Camp fire
⇒	Search
⊘	I'm waiting in the nearest house
⌒	Hill
┼	Go carefully
𝖾𝖺𝗌𝗍	East

One of the policemen has found a lost letter in the forest – but it's written in code! Use the key to work out what the letter says. It reveals where the crooks were planning to meet.

POLICE TRAINING

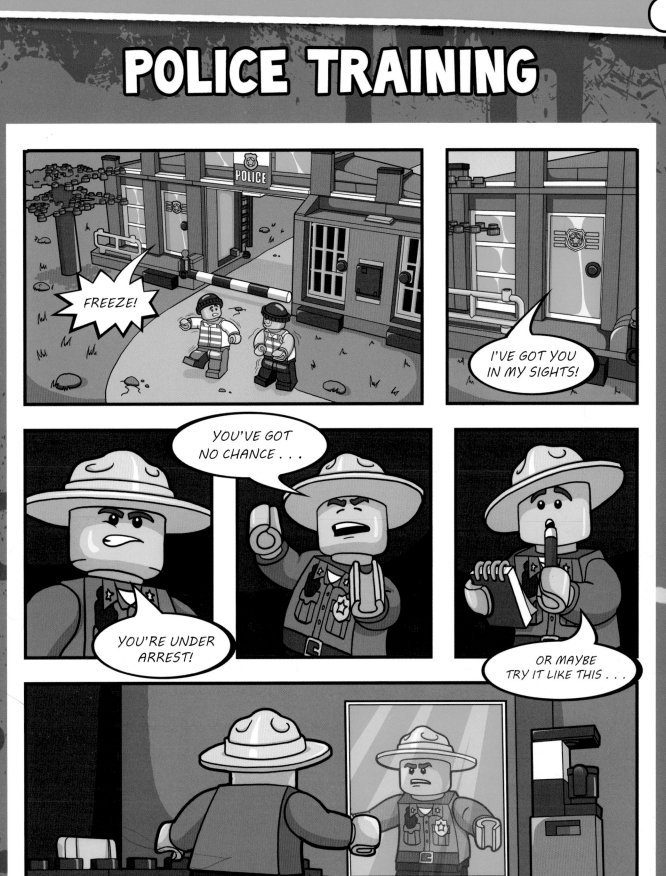

CONCERT IN THE PARK

Do you like music? Good, because the biggest pop stars in LEGO CITY are singing at the park today! Be careful, though – the biggest star of the criminal world is there, too! Can you spot the Red Scarf Crook hiding in the crowds?

Once you've found the crook, can you spot ten more details that make this picture different from the first?

SEA QUIZ

1.
A sea dog is:
a. A dog that lives in the sea.
b. A very experienced sailor.
c. A cunning fish dressed as a dog.

3.
A shark has very dangerous:
a. Tomatoes in the garden.
b. Teeth.
c. House furniture.

2.
A billow is:
a. A big wave.
b. The name of a LEGO CITY music band.
c. A singing snowman on a raft.

4.
In the port you can find:
a. Ships and boats.
b. Zebras and horses.
c. A football team.

Harry Seaweed and Steve Lifebelt love nothing more than to relax after work and quiz each other on their knowledge of the sea. Do you know all of the answers?

MAD BOARDS

The big windsurfing competition is coming, and each contestant dreams of having the coolest board. Use colouring pens or pencils to design a board of your very own!

LETTER IN A BOTTLE

One morning, Stan found a letter in a bottle asking for help.
It had instructions for how to get to a boat that had run out of fuel.
Read the instructions from the letter and help the fisherman get to the
stranded boat. Begin at the START square.

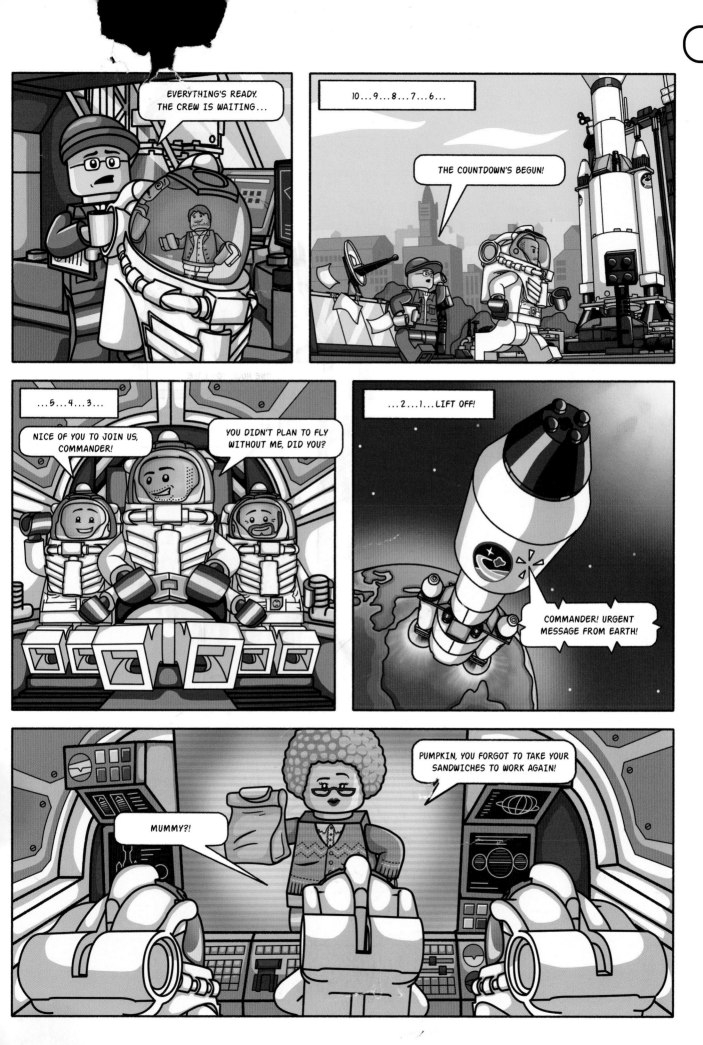

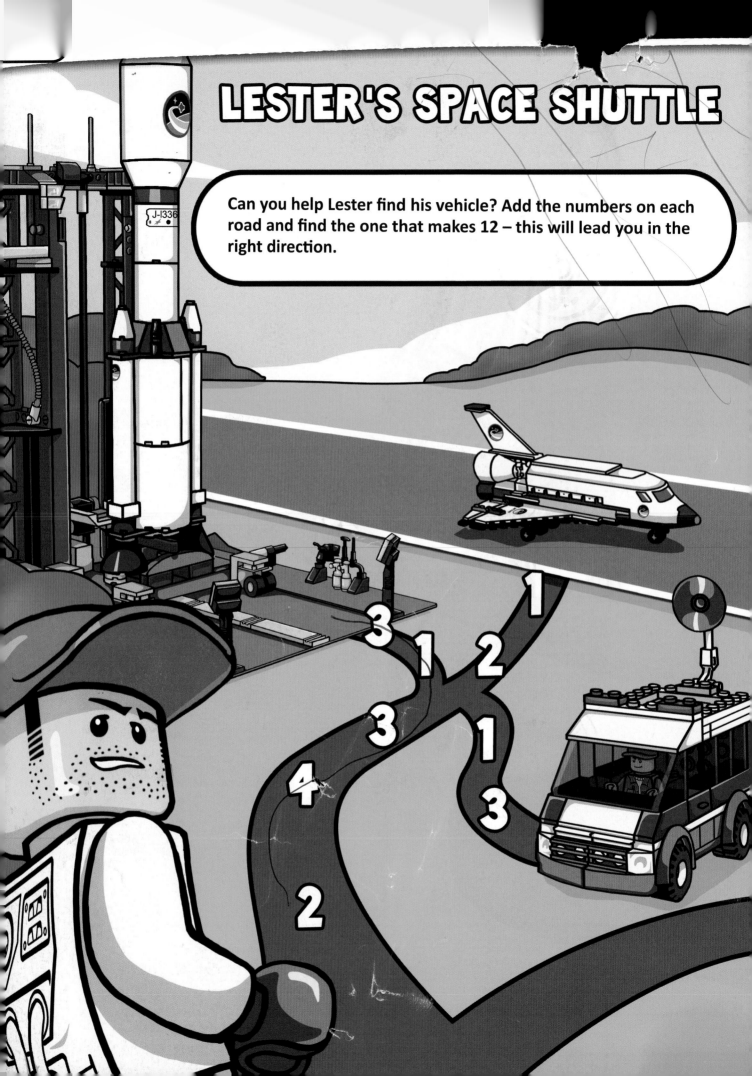

MAN ON THE MOON

A
R
G
N
S
O
M
T

a r m s t r o n g

Only astronauts who train for years and years can make the trip into space. Add the missing letters to the box above in order of size, from big to small, and discover who was the first person to land on the moon.

WHICH WAY?

These pieces of equipment all move in different ways - but they're missing their signs! Help the space centre workers to operate them properly by drawing the correct arrows in each empty sign.

TO THE MOON!

This astronaut is travelling to the moon. Can you help him pack for his journey? Tick all the objects he might need.

ALIEN PUZZLE

This puzzle is from an alien civilisation. Can you complete the square so that the sum of the numbers in each row equals 15?

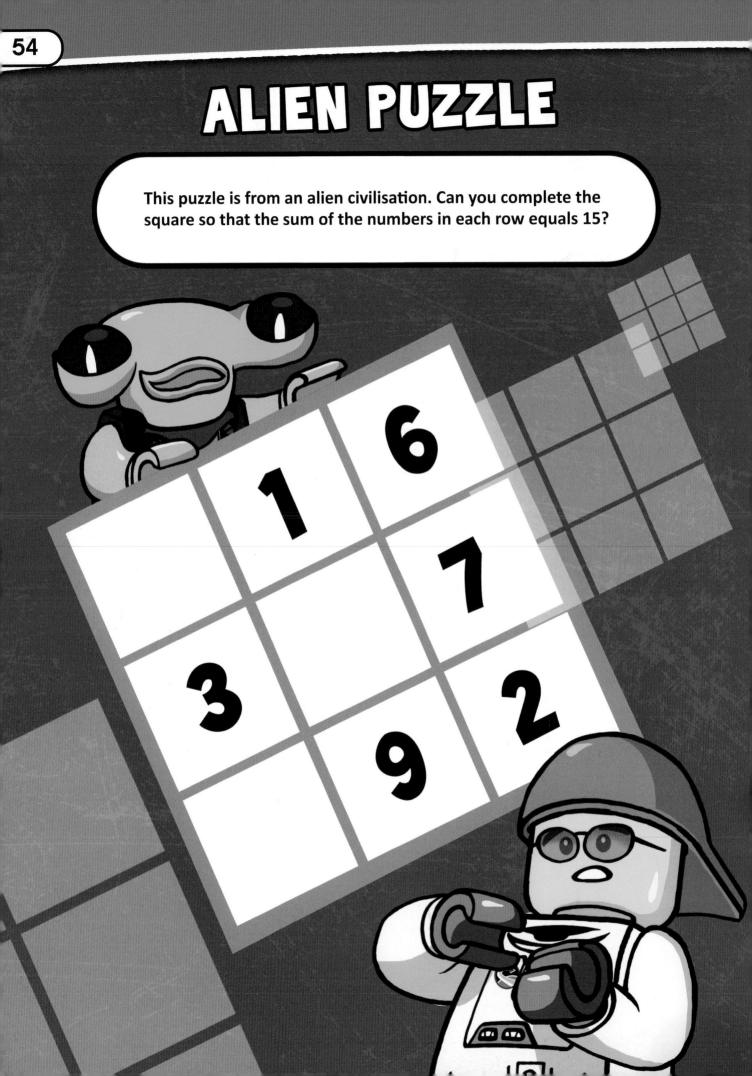

BUTTONS, BUTTONS, BUTTONS!

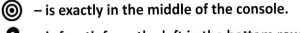

◎ – is exactly in the middle of the console.

? – is fourth from the left in the bottom row.

🌢 – is in the first row, second from the right.

Help Lester find the right buttons to press in the space shuttle. Using the clues above, draw in the symbols on the control panel in the cockpit.

Answers

p. 4 Police Puzzle

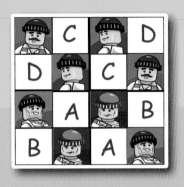

p. 6 Mysterious Vehicle

p. 10 Pizza Delivery Man

p. 11 Cheese Stretching!

p. 8-9 Sculpture contest

p. 12 Video Frame

p. 14-15 High-Speed Chase

1. b
2. b
3. b
4. a

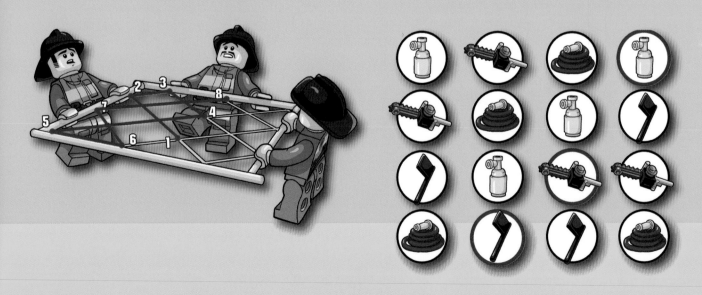

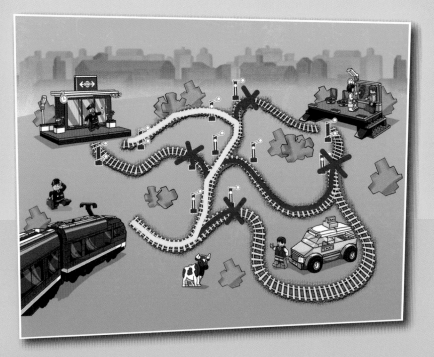
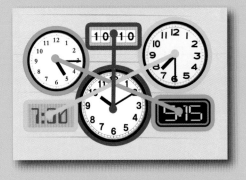

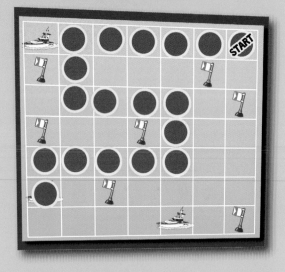

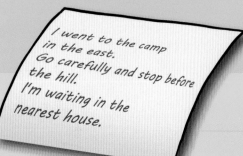
I went to the camp in the east.
Go carefully and stop before the hill.
I'm waiting in the nearest house.

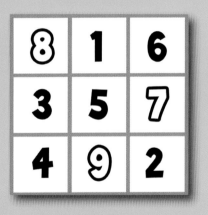

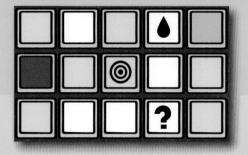